© 1997 Owl Records Ltd
Published by Geddes & Grosset, an imprint of
Children's Leisure Products Limited,
David Dale House, New Lanark, ML11 9DJ, Scotland,
for Owl Records Ltd, Dublin, Ireland

First printed 1997
Reprinted 1998, 1999, 2000

ISBN 1 85534 785 7

Printed and bound in Slovenia

IRISH LEGENDS

The Children of Lir

Retold by Reg Keating
Illustrated by Heather McKay

Tarantula Books

L ong ago in Ireland there lived a king named Lir. He lived with his wife and four children, and was very happy.

Lir's daughter was called Fionnuala. She was the eldest of the four children.

Fionnuala's three brothers were called Aodh, Fiachra and Conn.

They all lived in a beautiful castle in the middle of a forest.

When his wife died, Lir was very sad. The children were very sad too.

"My children need a mother,"
Lir said to himself. He decided
to marry again.

His new wife was called Aoife. Aoife
was very jealous of Lir's children. She
believed that Lir loved his children more
than he loved her.

Aoife hated the children so much that
she longed to get rid of them.

Soon, she thought of a plan.

One warm summer's day, she took Fionnuala and her brothers to swim in the lake near the castle.

The children were delighted. There was nothing they liked better than to play in the water.

They spent hours in the lake, playing together happily. They splashed each other and sang at the top of their voices.

S uddenly, Aoife took out a magic
wand. She waved it in the air.

There was a flash of light, and the
children of Lir were nowhere to be seen.

Instead, there were four beautiful swans
in the water, with feathers as white as
snow.

The children looked at each other in
horror.

They had been turned into swans!

"What have you done to us?" cried Fionnuala.

"I have put you under a spell", said Aoife. "You will be swans for nine hundred years!" she laughed.

"You will spend three hundred years here in Lough Derravaragh. Then you must spend three hundred years in the Sea of Moyle. And you will spend the last three hundred years in the waters of Inish Glora," she said.

"You will remain as swans for nine hundred years, until a Christian bell heralds a new age." Aoife said.

Aoife then returned to the castle. She told Lir that his children had drowned.

The king rushed to the lake, but he could see no sign of his children.

All he could see was four white swans swimming towards him.

Suddenly, one of the swans called his name!

It was Fionnuala. She told her father what had happened. The king was very angry. He punished his wicked wife by turning her into a large, ugly moth.

The moth flew high into the sky and disappeared forever.

Lir visited his children every day. They talked and sang to him, and were quite happy.

Lir brought them food from the castle.

He would often stay with them until sunset. He told them stories and taught them many new songs.

When Lir died, the children were very sad. They did not sing any more. They felt very lonely.

After three hundred years in Lough Derravaragh, the swans flew to the Sea of Moyle.

It was very cold there. There were huge waves and great storms. Sometimes the swans were frightened. They longed for the warm waters of Lough Derravaragh.

Fionnuala and her brothers spent three hundred years on the Sea of Moyle. Then the time came for their final journey.

When they reached Inish Glora, they were very tired.

Early one morning, the swans heard the sound of a bell.

They saw a man dressed in a long cloak. He was a monk who lived on the island. He was ringing a bell to call people to pray.

The swans were excited at the sound of the bell. The terrible spell would soon be over.

They swam over to the monk.

"Is that a Christian bell?" asked Fionnuala.

The monk was very surprised to hear a swan speak.

Fionnuala told him their story.

The monk listened carefully to the sad story of the Children of Lir.

When Fionnuala had finished telling their story, the monk raised his hand to bless the swans.

As soon as he touched them, their beautiful white feathers disappeared.

When the monk looked up, he saw a lovely young girl and three tall, handsome young men.

Fionnuala and her brothers looked at each other and saw that they were no longer swans. They danced and sang with delight.

The children had been swans for exactly nine hundred years. The wicked Aoife's spell was broken.

Fionnuala and her brothers decided to return to Lough Derravaragh.

The castle was still there, as beautiful as before.

From then on, they lived happily. They played in the forest and swam in the lake, Fionnuala, Aodh, Fiachra and Conn, the Children of Lir.